隆！隆！我們起程去！
Brrmm! Let's Go!

Julie Kingdon
Illustrated by Leo Broadley

Chinese translation by Sylvia Denham

Mantra Lingua

我是莉安，我坐在爸爸的腳踏車後面。
我們起程去！

I'm Lian and I ride on the back
of Daddy's bicycle.

bring

briiing!

Let's go!

我是約翰，我正坐在爸爸的拖拉車上穿過農田。
我們起程去！

My name's John. I'm riding through the fields on Dad's tractor.

Rumble-grumble judder-trundle!

Let's go!

我的名字是花達，我正坐在我姐姐的雪車。
我們起程去！

I'm Falda and I'm whizzing along on my big sister's snow-mobile.

Vrmmm Vrmmm

Varrooooom!

Let's go!

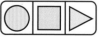

我的名字是露茜亞，爸爸和我在他的威尼斯平底船上正在水上滑行。我們起程去！

My name's Lucia. My daddy and I glide through the water in his gondola.

Splash splish swoosh swish!

Let's Go!

我是莎娜，我是坐在姨母的水上飛機到岸的。
我們起程去！

I'm Sera and I'm landing on the water in my aunty's seaplane.

Niiiaaaww woosh judder judder Sploosh!

Let's go!

我的名字是莉絲，哥哥和我正在乘搭
計程車。
我們起程去！

My name's Lizzie. My brother and I
are riding in a taxi.

beeeep

beeeep!

Let's Go!

我是尼蘭，我正坐在叔父的
三輪摩托車回家。
我們起程去！

I'm Niran and I'm riding home on my
uncle's tuk-tuk.

Honk honk

bounce **brake!**

Let's go!

我的名字是杜米路，我可以跟媽媽坐她的直升機。
我們起程去！

My name is Tumelo. I can fly with my mum in her helicopter.

Swish swish whirr vrrrum!

Let's Go!

我是馬薩克，我是坐在由愛斯基摩
狗拉動的雪橇橫過雪地的。
我們起程去！

I'm Massak and I'm zooming across
the snow on a sledge pulled by huskies.

Woof woof
whiiiiiiiizzzzzz!

Let's go!

我的名字是阿潘，我正在
火車上橫越城鎮。
我們起程去！

My name's Arpan. I'm travelling
through the country on a train.

Clickerty
clickerty
clackerty
Whooooooooooooosh!

Let's go!

我是撒豪，我正坐在爸爸的摩托車。
我們起程去！

I'm Zahur and I'm riding on my dad's
motorbike.

PHUT PHUT

VVRRRRROOOOOM!

LET'S GO!

Key words

I   bicycle   ride   my

glide   sledge   travel   aunty   mum

train   brother   fly   can   snow-mobile   in

uncle   with   gondola   seaplane   tractor

tuk-tuk   the   on   helicopter

motorbike   taxi

Children from around
the world introduce the different
forms of transport that they use. Trucks,
trains, tuk-tuks, gondolas… Follow along as
the pacy, onomatopoeic text races from
Alabama to Zurich!

The Our Lives, Our World series explores the
rich diversity of children's lives and develops
a worldwide perspective.
With RecorderPEN you can listen to narrations
and discover words and sounds on each page.
Children, parents and practitioners
can record their own journeys
page by page.

Other titles in the series: Yum! Let's Eat! ◆ Goal! Let's Play!

Brrmm! Let's Go! is available in 11 dual language editions:
English with Arabic, Bengali, Czech, Chinese (Cantonese), Chinese Simplified
(Mandarin), French, Polish, Portuguese, Spanish, Russian or Urdu.
Also available in English only.

For a full list of audio files, please refer to: www.mantralingua.com

TalkingPEN™

MANTRA LINGUA
Listen, record, play…

CANTON
& ENGLI

978-1-84611

9 781846 115

O5-IGS-528

Alfriston Clergy House

(*Front cover*) The Clergy House from
Alfriston village green

(*Opposite*) The entrance front

(*Back cover*) The Clergy House in ruins.
The National Trust's first appeal, in 1896,
got off to a slow start